CW00385105

Boyling Point 2

more political cartoons
by Frank Boyle

ARGYLL ✠ PUBLISHING

© Frank Boyle 2011

First published 2011
Argyll Publishing
Glendaruel
Argyll PA22 3AE
Scotland
www.argyllpublishing.co.uk

The author has asserted his moral rights.

**British Library Cataloguing-in-Publication Data.
A catalogue record for this book is available
from the British Library.**

ISBN 978 1 906134 81 5

Printing Bell & Bain Ltd, Glasgow

to two of my teachers,
Joe Rafferty and Grant Clifford

Contents

Foreword

FOLLOW me into Frank Boyle's heid. No need for torches. It'll be dark when first we squeeze through but, behold, suddenly all is illuminated: lummy, there's a whole urban landscape in here, a city full of tenements, townhouses, suburbs, estates, institutions, castles, dumps, department stores, malls, buses, taxis, invisible trams, thoroughfares, galleries, museums, parliaments and footer stadia.

And, lo, these are full of neds, toffs, Hibees, Jambos, cheery shoppers, weary passengers, leary drivers, lunching ladies, comical cooncillors, binmen, statesmen, polismen, cabbies, shysters, flysters, revellers, moaners, and just plain bewildered bystanders. They're all here, in this cornucopia of cartoonery.

A great city demands a great cartoonist, and Edinburgh is so lucky to have Frank. His column on the Edinburgh Evening News shines like a star on steroids.

We turn to him as to a beacon of hope: 'Frank, Embra's doin' ma nut in. Please put it into perspective and gie's a laugh at the same time.' Here, political enemies and football rivals are humanised, made to seem like two cheeks of the same bottom, as it were. Here,

caricatures are instantly recognisable, not just local worthies but national heroes as well, whether it be the First Eck or fair-to-middling statesmen further afield at yon Wastemonster in Englandshire.

Here, het-up arguments are rightly reduced to revelry. And the revel is in the detail, not just the faces of folk or daft things they might wear, but in the familiar architecture, from the world-famous landmarks to the grim tenements of the New Town and the subtly magnificent schemes.

This is Edinburgh: no fur coats but a lot of pants. The best laid plans of mice and mentalists – the bams' tram springs to mind – are dissected with the sharpest tool of all: the wand of humour. The ability to make people laugh is a form of magic. You can see the spell cast on folk reading Frank's latest, as they ride on the bus all the way from Little France to the Champs Eh Leithie. So, assuming you've spared no expense in purchasing this book, come with me as we dig up some roads and follow the imaginary tramlines through Frank's heid.

Robert McNeil
October 2011

2007/08

Tony Blair became a Catholic.

Ian Wilmut, one of the scientists who cloned Dolly the sheep, spoke out in favour of the Union.
Jack McConnell grew up on a sheep farm on Arran.

The people of Iraq paid a heavy price for the invasion of their country.

Tony Blair failed to congratulate Alex Salmond on winning the Holyrood election.
He then met Gaddafi in the Libyan desert.

Hibs are looking for a new manager.
Kenny Ritchie, who spent years on death row in the USA, arrives back in Edinburgh.

Calton district in Glasgow's east end has male life expectancy of 54.
Celtic lost 4-2 at home to Rangers.

Alex Salmond wants a separate Scottish Olympic team.
Obesity hits recored levels in Scotland.

Chris de Burgh becomes the first western singer to appear in Iran since the 1979 revolution.

The SNP are criticised for being too supportive of Donald Trump and his controversial plans for a golf course in Aberdeenshire. Led Zeppelin play a reunion concert in London.

Labour MSP Andy Kerr is interviewed by police after accepting undeclared hospitality from McDonald's.

Fidel Castro stands down as Cuban leader. Tommy Sheridan is jobless since losing his seat as an MSP.

Donald Trump promised that wildlife will be protected on his new golf course in Aberdeenshire.

Celtic goalkeeper Artur Boruc allows the ball to slip through his hands
in a match against Hibs at Easter Road.

2009

Gordon Brown was behind in the polls.
Michael Jackson announced plans for a series of concerts in London.

Anthony Gormley, sculptor of the Angel of the North, is to do a series of sculptures for the banks of the Water of Leith.

Hitachi won the contract to build trains for the East Coast line.

Gordon Brown was very unpopular. Susan Boyle made her debut on 'Britain's got Talent'.

On the 65th anniversary of D-Day, two BNP members were elected to the European Parliament.

Edinburgh Festival organisers want to attract more people from Glasgow to the Festival.

OVER A BARREL.

OUTRAGE AT MacASKILL VERDICT

bp

The Scottish government is criticised for releasing the terminally ill Lockerbie bomber but both Tony Blair and Gordon Brown had already met Col. Gadaffi and BP has signed an oil deal with Libya.

Diageo, the makers of Johnnie Walker whisky, reject Finance Secretary John Swinney's attempt to save 500 jobs in Kilmarnock and Glasgow.

A large group of Romanians were forced out of their homes by a mob in Belfast.

Several members of the House of Lords were alleged to have taken bribes.

Shettleston in Glasgow is the heaviest drinking part of the UK.
John Swinney cancelled the Glasgow Airport rail link.

Marvin Andrews returned to play for Raith Rovers.
He was also a Christian preacher and claimed he was cured of injury by divine intervention.

Little Cumbrae, an island in the Clyde, is to be turned into a centre for yoga and meditation.

David Miliband backs Tony Blair for European President. A large dinosaur skeleton is discovered.

BNP leader Nick Griffin was controversially invited to appear on 'Question Time'.

The SNP lost the Glasgow North East by-election in the same week that Jedward were voted off the X Factor. Alex Salmond is known as Eck.

John Swinney's cancellation of the Glasgow Airport rail link led to claims that the SNP had an anti-Glasgow agenda. A whale was spotted swimming in the Clyde near Glasgow city centre.

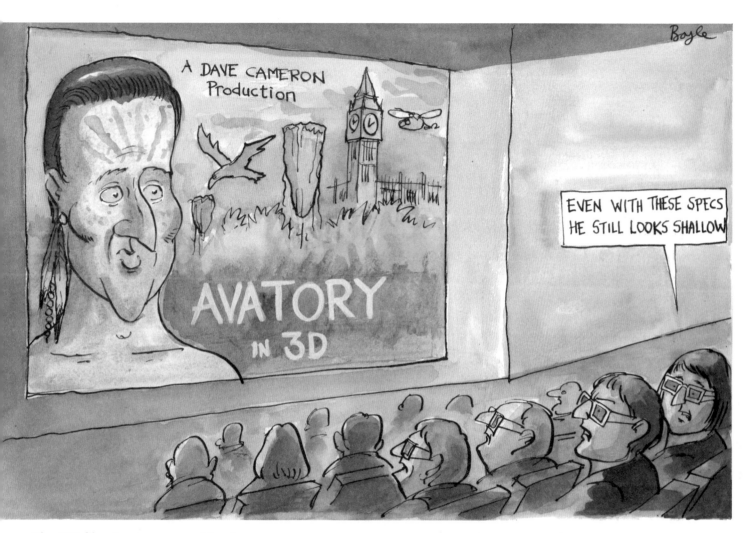

The 3D film Avatar opened in cinemas.

The cost of the 2014 Commonwealth Games in Glasgow keeps going up.

Alex Salmond flies to Copenhagen to meet Arnold Swarzenegger at the G8 conference.

A strike at British Airways led to negotiations between BA and Unite, the union representing cabin crew.

2010

After stepping down as Prime Minister Tony Blair embarked on a lucrative speaking tour.

Annabel Goldie vowed to defeat the SNPs Referendum Bill.
Tim Burton's film of Alice in Wonderland opened.

Plans to privatise Scotland's search and rescue service were announced.

Former Labour MPs John Reid, Helen Liddell, Jack McConnell and John Prescott took their seats in the House of Lords.

Edinburgh Airport introduced a £1 dropping-off charge for motorists.

The Scheme, a controversial documentary about a housing estate in Kilmarnock, was shown on TV. Former Tory minister Lord Forsyth criticised 'dole scroungers'.

Lothian buses are to be painted a shade of maroon known as madder.
Hibs were knocked out of the Scottish Cup by Ross County.

A moving film of a dying chimp being cared for by other chimps was shown on TV.
Gordon Brown was heading for defeat in the general election.

Despite the unpopularity of the Labour government there was no sign of a Tory revival in Scotland.

A tanned Tony Blair took time off from his lucrative engagements to help launch the Labour Party election campaign. The slogan was 'A future fair for all'.

Gordon Brown was seen as having performed poorly in the first of the leaders debates.
Lord Mandelson was running the Labour campaign.

The Scottish Conservatives failed to increase their vote.
Michael Caine voiced his support for David Cameron.

BNP leader Nick Griffin stood for parliament in the Barking constituency.

Alex Salmond was excluded from the leaders debates on TV during the UK general election.
He admitted to being a keen Star Trek fan.

Following the inconclusive election result, Gordon Brown tried to form a coalition with the LibDems.

After the election Nick Clegg had to chose to form a coalition with Labour or the Tories.

The Scottish Tories failed to improve on their total of one MP.
BP were responsible for a major oil leak in the Gulf of Mexico.

The Tories and LibDems formed a coalition and Clegg and Cameron appeared at a joint press conference.

The Evening News introduced a spot-the-ball competition and trouble followed at an Edinburgh derby match. A flare and coins were thrown on the pitch.

The Church of England was split over the issue of women bishops.
During the hunt for the killer Raoul Moat in Northumberland, Paul Gasgoine offered
to act as an intermediary.

Brian Souter, Stagecoach owner and major SNP donor, tested out an amphibious bus on the Clyde.

During the World Cup, an octopus called Paul had correctly predicted the winners of several matches.

Iain Duncan Smith promised to crack down on 'dole scroungers'.

John Prescott, a former critic of the House of Lords, accepted a peerage.

Sighting of UFOs were reported over West Lothian.
Hibs were knocked out of the Europa League in the qualifying round.

Vince Cable supported higher tuition fees despite his party's election promise not to raise them.
The Man Booker prize winner was announced.

The cost of the ill-fated Edinburgh trams scheme continues to rocket.
The aircraft carrier Ark Royal was scrapped.

The Pope visited Edinburgh and toured the streets in the Popemobile.

Scotland was shown to be statistically the heaviest drinking part of the UK.

Tony Blair's memoirs were published. He said he had no regrets about the invasion of Iraq.

Prince Charles arrived in Edinburgh aboard the Royal Train to promote a 'Go green' message.

Annabel Goldie said the Tories had no reason to apologise for the Thatcher years.
The Camera Obscura in Edinburgh held an exhibition of distorting mirrors.

It was rumoured that the Hobbit might be filmed in Scotland.

Jimmy Reid, the former trade union leader, died. During the UCS shipyard work-in of 1971 he warned workers, in a famous speech, that there would be no bevvying.
Nicola Sturgeon unsuccessfully tried to introduce a minimum price for alcohol.

Rangers were in financial difficulties. For a while Lloyds TSB bank were effectively running the club.

Plans were announced to sell off Coulport naval weapons base to US arms firm Lockheed Martin.

It was feared that closure of several coastguard stations could cost lives.

Some residents of Edinburgh's New Town were opposed to the introduction of large wheelie bins on their streets.

Labour's Jim Murphy said he wasn't aware that an known criminal had been at his fundraising event. Several Labour figures had recently been forced to stand down after scandals.

Edinburgh's trams fiasco was described as 'hell on wheels'.
The proposed route was much shorter than originally planned.

Ryanair planned to charge passengers £1 to use the toilet on the plane.

Trainspotting author Irvine Welsh attacked Scotland's drinking culture.

Transport minister Stewart Stevenson resigned
after heavy snow brought chaos to Scotland's transport network.

Alex Salmond commissioned Jack Vettriano to produce his Christmas card.
It showed a couple doing the Twist.

2011

Alex Salmond met Chinese deputy prime minister in Edinburgh.
Former Scottish Socialist Party leader Tommy Sheridan was jailed.

Rioters caused damage in London following an anti-cuts demo.

Hibs went through a bad patch, failing to score a goal in January 2011.

David Cameron was accused of using his trip to the Middle East to promote British arm sales to repressive regimes.

Edinburgh zoo awaits the arrival of two pandas from China.
LibDem support slumps following their coalition with the Tories.

Stagecoach owner Brian Souter donates £500,000 to the SNP.

David Cameron's 'Big society' plans would result in the loss of public service jobs.

Labour leader Ed Miliband appoints Ed Balls as Shadow Chancellor.
Peter Mullan's new film Neds is released.

Hibs were playing very badly.
Edinburgh Zoo announced that two pandas would be arriving from China on loan.

The opposition parties defeated John Swinney's supermarket tax.
All had received donations from major supermarket chains.

Local government organisation, COSLA condemned election promises as being like junk food.

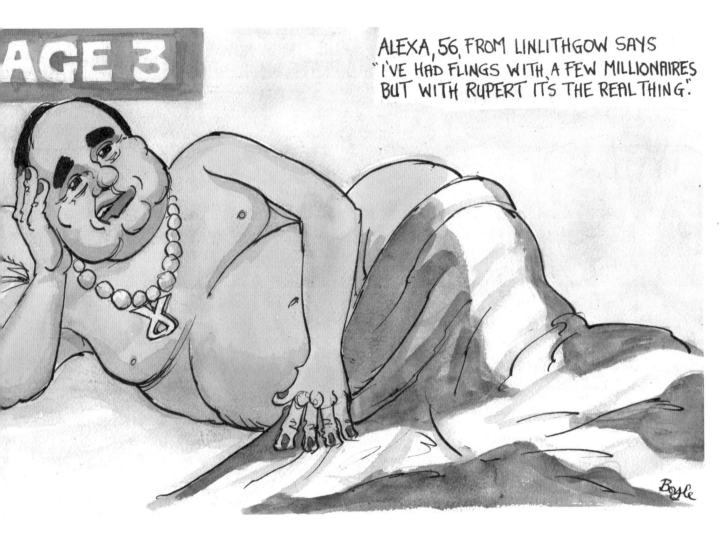

The Scottish edition of the Sun backed the SNP.

Iain Gray was accosted by demonstrators at Glasgow Central Station.
He took refuge in a Subway sandwich shop.

Midge Ure played a benefit gig for the SNP.

Eddie Izzard campaigned with Labour's Iain Gray.

Mark Millar, author of the comic book KickAss, pledged support for the SNP.

On the eve of the election Iain Gray set off on a marathon 40 hour campaigning tour of Scotland.

The LibDems suffered their own Highland clearance when they lost all their MSPs in the north of Scotland.

The number of LibDem MSPs dropped to 5 after the election.

Jim Murphy was appointed to head an inquiry into Labour's disastrous election result in which several well known MSPs lost their seats. STV cancelled Taggart.

On Bob Dylan's 70th birthday, high winds caused disruption to Scotrail services.

Willie Rennie became the new leader of the Scottish Liberal Democrats.

The Archbishop of Canterbury attacked the policies of the coalition government.

The Bahrain Grand Prix was set to go ahead despite the deaths of pro-democracy protesters there. It was cancelled at the last minute.

Rupert Murdoch appeared before the House of Commons inquiry into phone hacking.

Rupert Murdoch closed down the News of the World following the phone hacking scandal.

Scotrail passengers complained of overcrowding on the Glasgow-Edinburgh trains during the Edinburgh Festival.

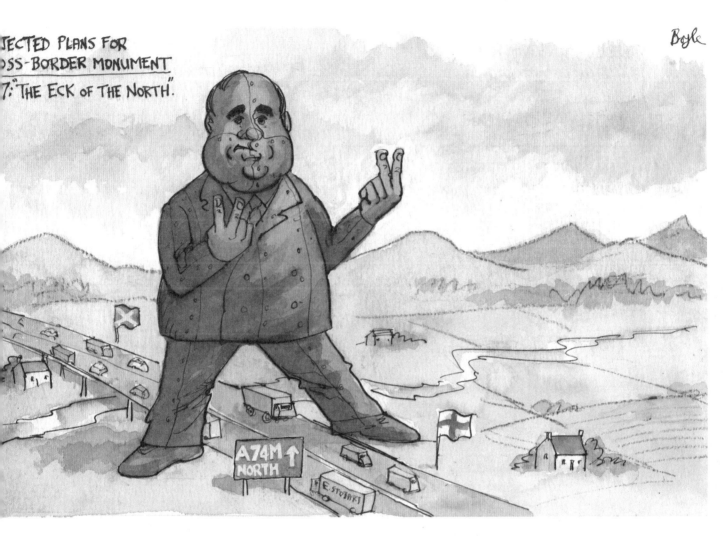

Plans were unveiled for a monument to mark the Border between Scotland and England.

Former RBS boss Sir Fred Goodwin went to court to stop news of an extramarital affair becoming public.

Edinburgh Council leaders Steve Cardownie and Jenny Dawe face a motion of no confidence. Gaddafi refuses to step down in Libya.

David Miliband was accused of plotting against his brother Ed.
Brad Pitt was making a Zombie film in Glasgow.
The Inverclyde by-election was called.

Councillors vote to end the proposed tram line at Haymarket rather than St. Andrew's Square.
All Scottish football teams were knocked out of Europe before the end of August.

Under proposed new anti-sectarian laws making the Sign of the Cross might be seen as offensive in some circumstances.

A 'Little Venice' development is planned on the Union Canal at Fountainbridge.

Edinburgh Royal Infirmary, which was built under the private finance initiative (PFI), was criticised for poor hygiene standards.

www.boylecartoon.co.uk

twitter.com/boylecartoon